Usborne

Doodle Pad for Girls

Illustrated by
Maria Pearson and Lizzie Barber

Written by Kirsteen Robson

Designed by Karen Tomlins

Transform these shapes into cats.

Doodle patterns the skaters have made.

Doodle a wild tornado.

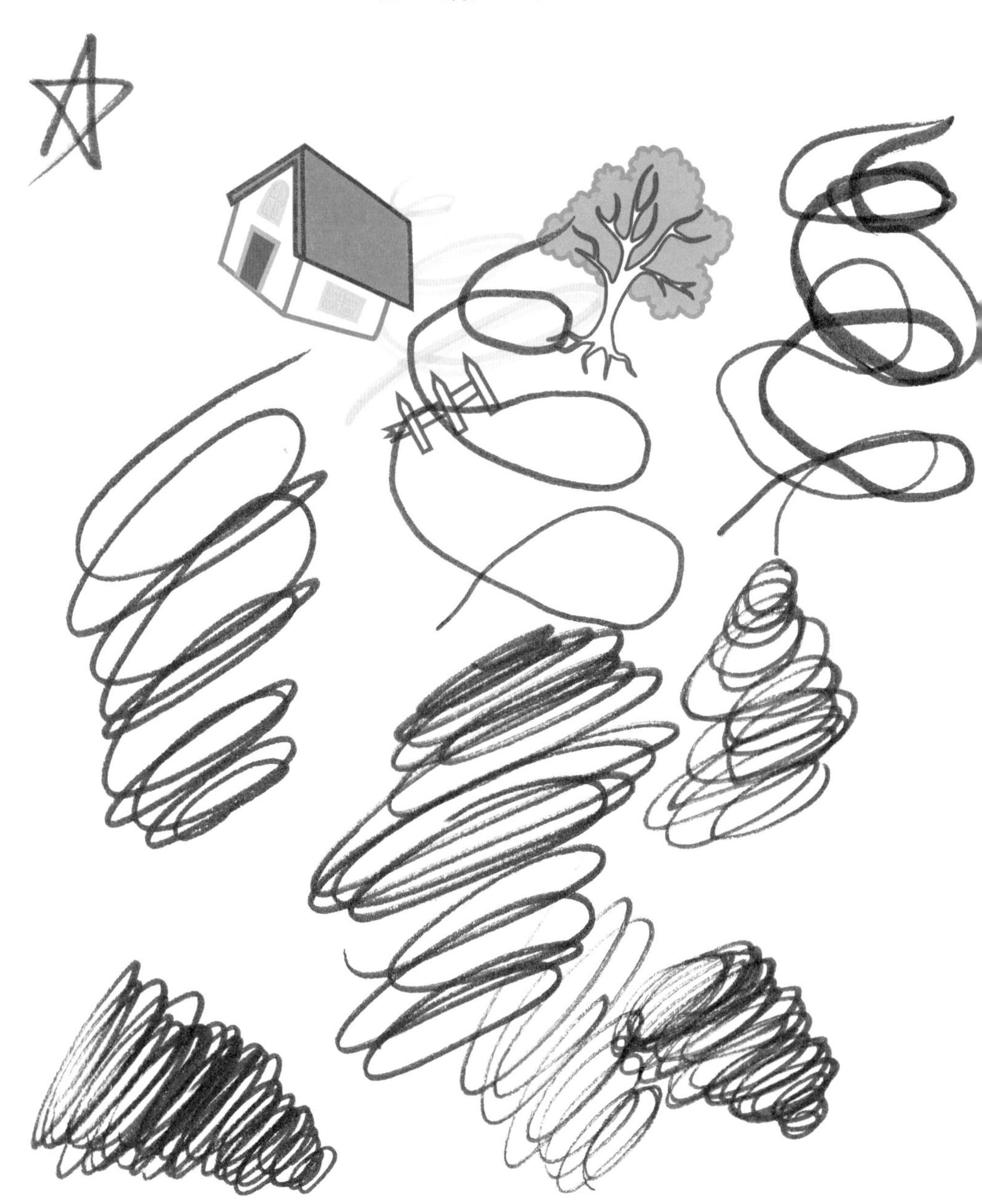

Add patterns to the sails.

Doodle patterns in these shapes.

Doodle scales on the fish.

Draw more snowmen.

to Mum I am so glad
you are Home I missed
you so much I tride to
call you but you wolde
pick up anyway Love
you so much Lots of Love
Imy

Doodle patterns on the fruity shapes.

Design a robot.

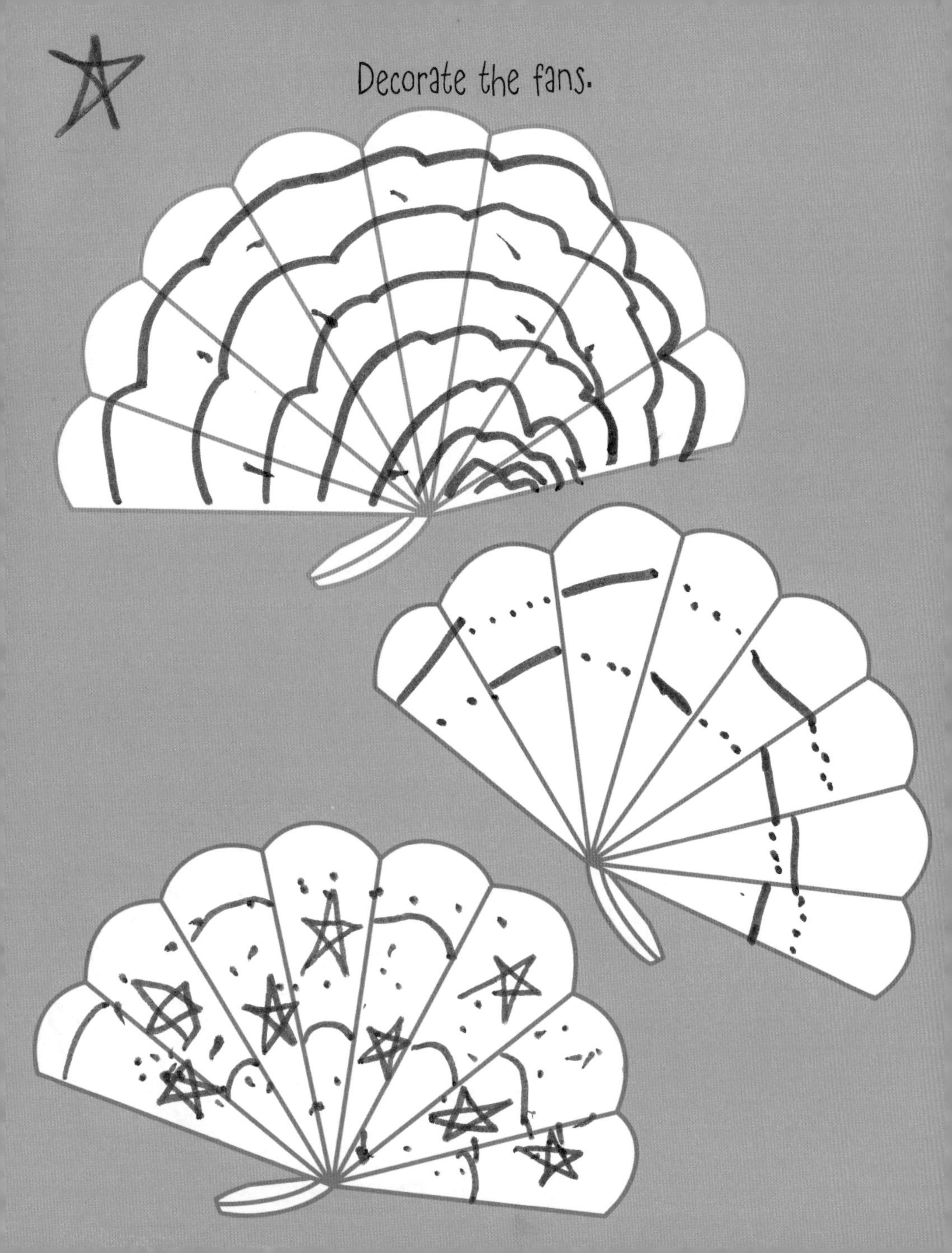
Decorate the fans.

Decorate the shoes and design some more of your own.

Decorate the snails' shells.

Transform these circles into anything you like.

Fill these shapes with stripes.

Draw more birds on the branches.

Doodle a surprising catch on the line.

Doodle something appearing out of the magician's hat.

Give the chicks eyes, beaks and legs.

Doodle some noodles, then decorate the bowl.

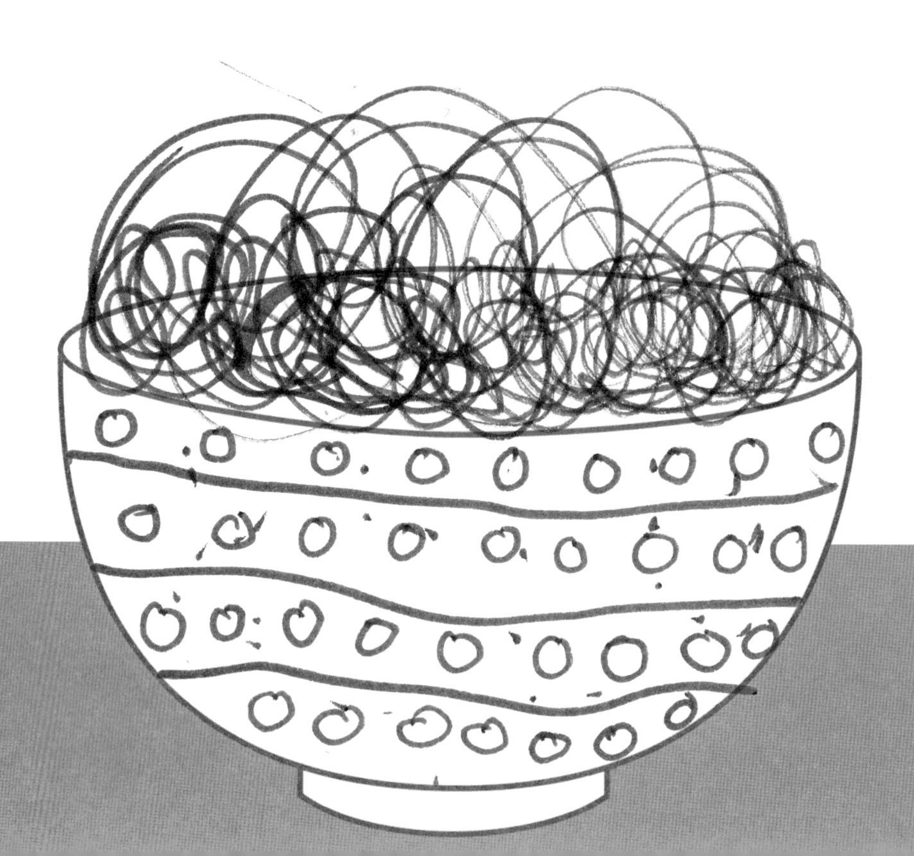

Make these shapes into birds.

Doodle ski tracks in the mountain snow.

Design some outrageous sunglasses.

Make the swirly doodle grow.

Decorate the elephants.

Doodle some footprints in the snow.

Add finishing touches to the wedding cake.

Add birds or eggs to the nest.

Draw what might be standing on the plinths and pedestals.

Complete this dinosaur.

Think of a title for this book then design a cover for it.

Doodle patterns on the socks.

Doodle designs on the beach clothes.

Fill the page with butterflies.

Turn these shapes into trucks, buses and cars.

Doodle aliens in the craters.

Transform these clouds into animals.

Turn these slugs into snails by designing homes for them.

Doodle patterns on the Russian dolls.

Doodle some waves.

Doodle spots and stripes on the beetles.

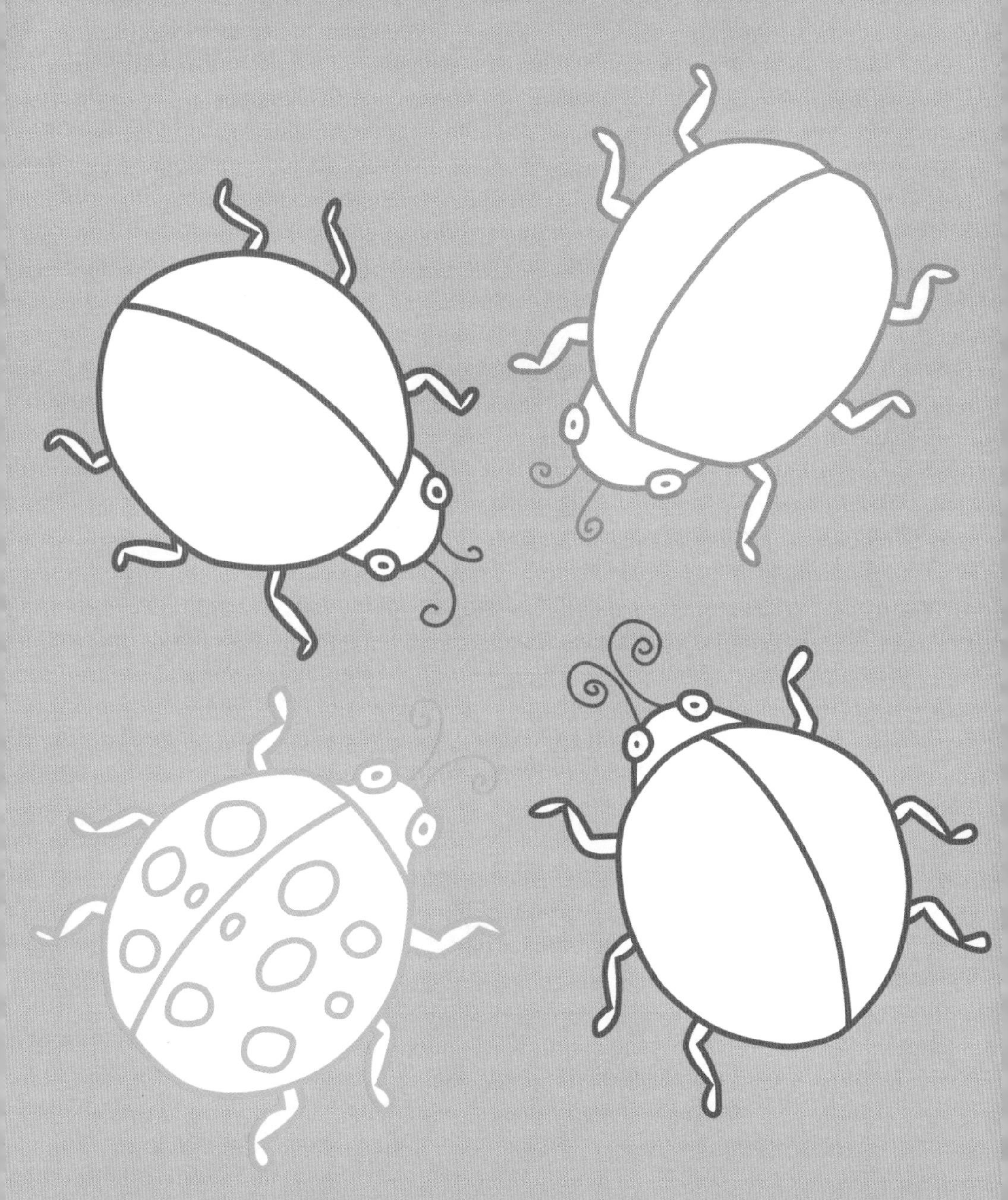

Doodle patterns on the butterflies.

Decorate the lollipops.

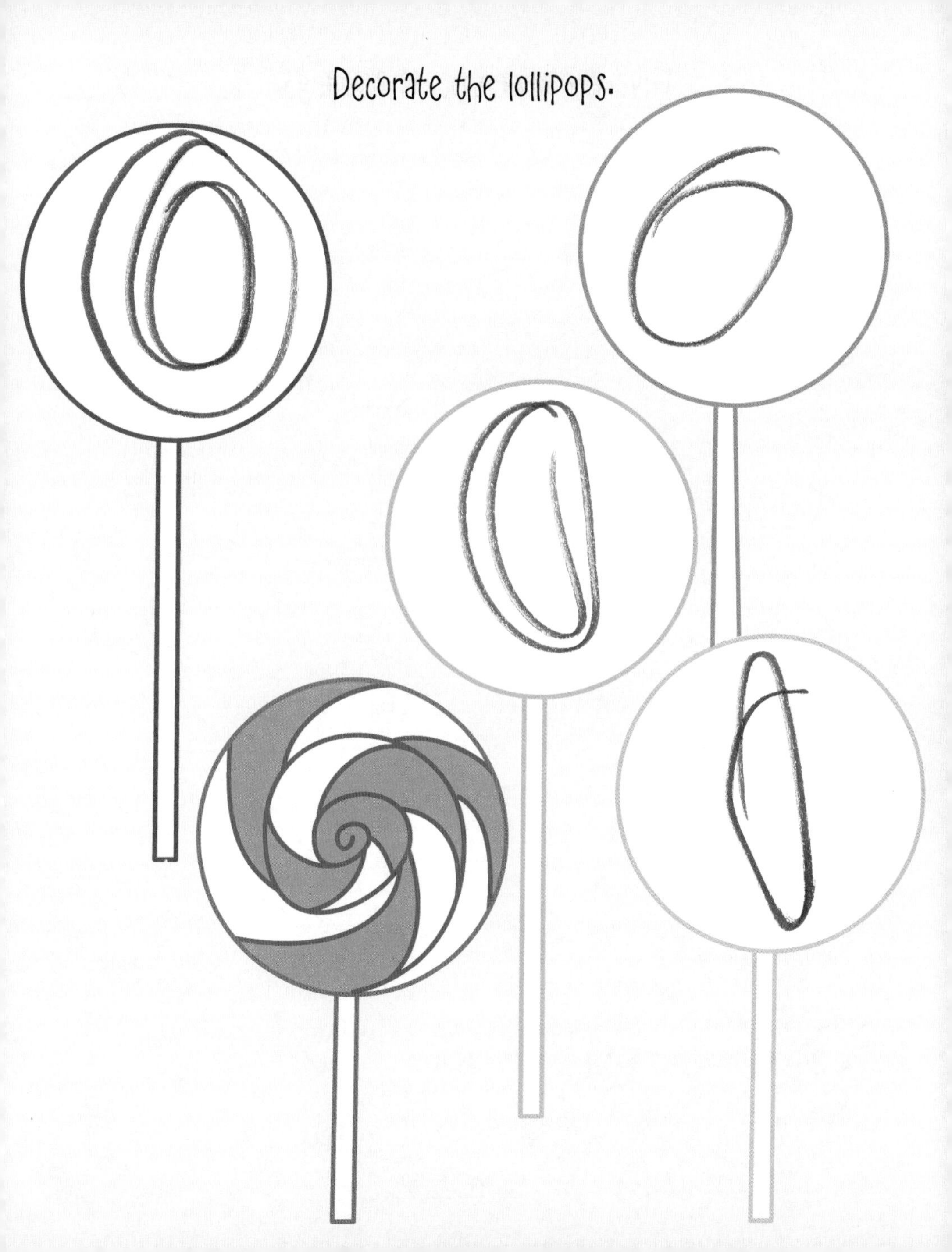

Give the sheep heads and legs.

Doodle wheels, windows and people to turn these rectangles into buses.

Draw something you might see under a magnifying glass.

Design a castle.

Decorate the party masks.

Decorate the shapes and add some more.

Draw triangles inside triangles, inside triangles...

Decorate the flower and leaf shapes.

Make the bottom dinosaur look like the top one.

Doodle the shapes into birds.

Doodle a daisy chain.

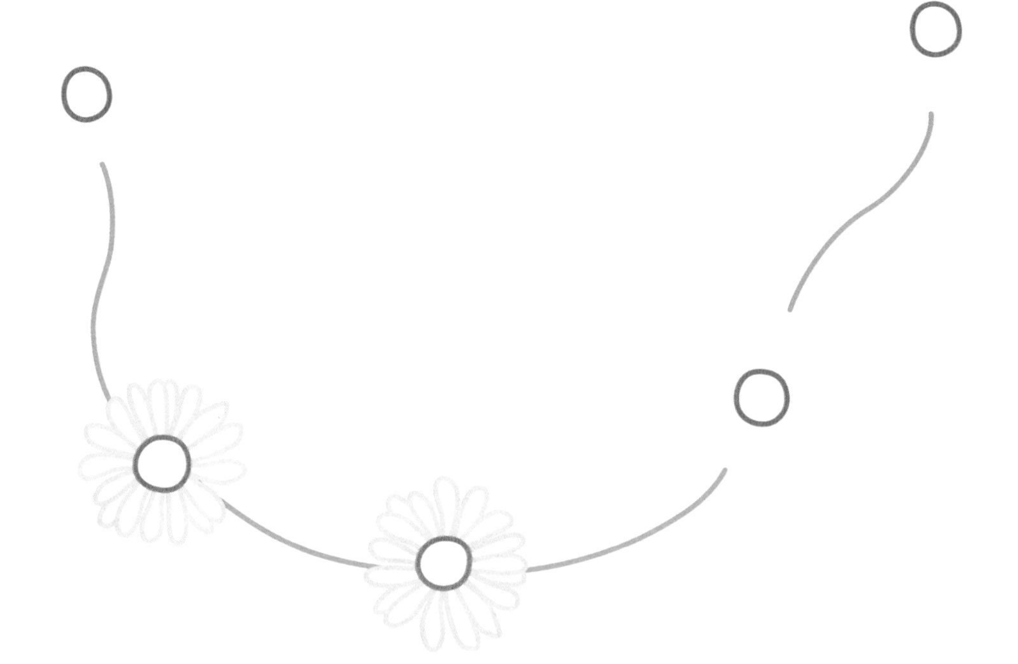

Give these caterpillars boots.

Add swirls of smoke to the chimneys.

Doodle a spectacular fountain.

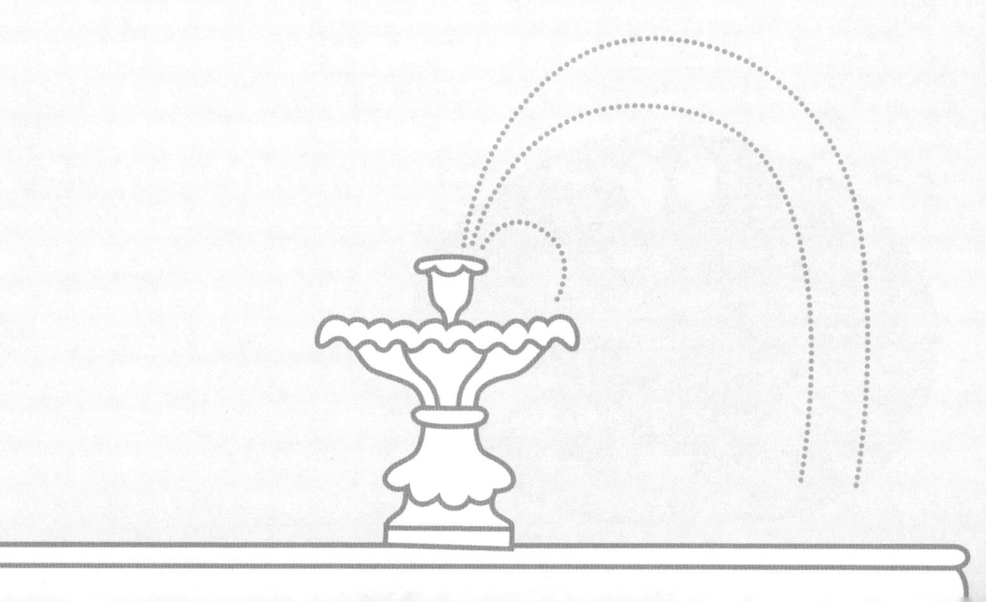

Draw a pond, then doodle some ripples and fish
and fill the sky with dragonflies.

Add more parachutes and skydivers.

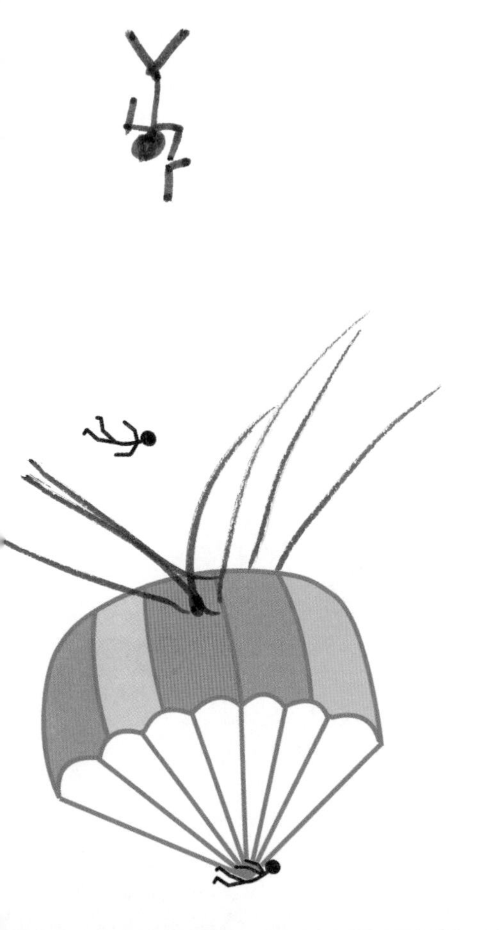

Add more ants to the march.

Decorate the cookies.

Add rain, snow and lightning to the clouds.

Turn these shapes into trees.

Fill the page with buttons.

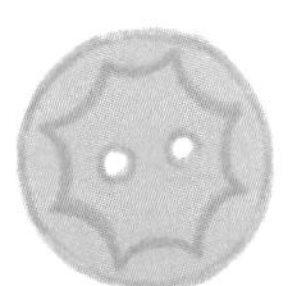

Draw what might be chasing these little dinosaurs.

Doodle a crazy science experiment.

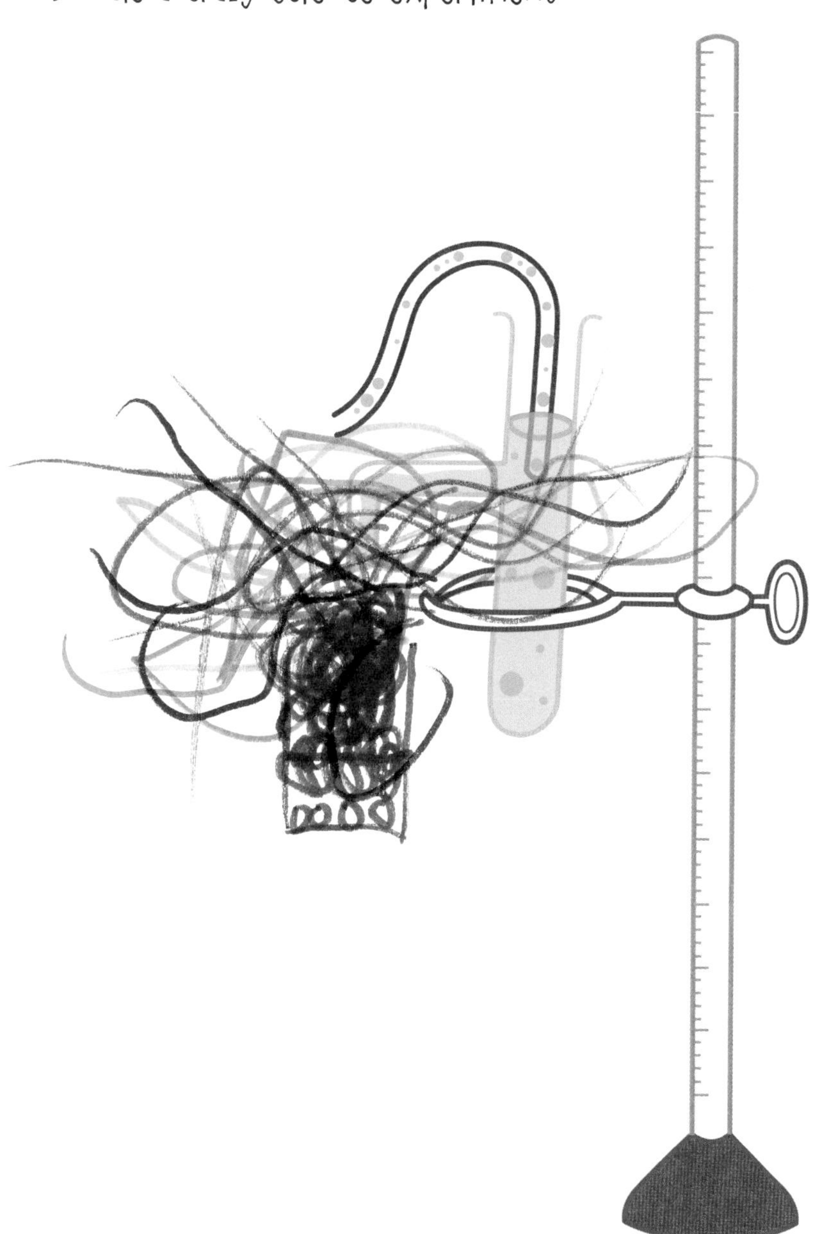

Draw the dream.

Use your pen to make the enchanted forest grow.

Add details to the boats.

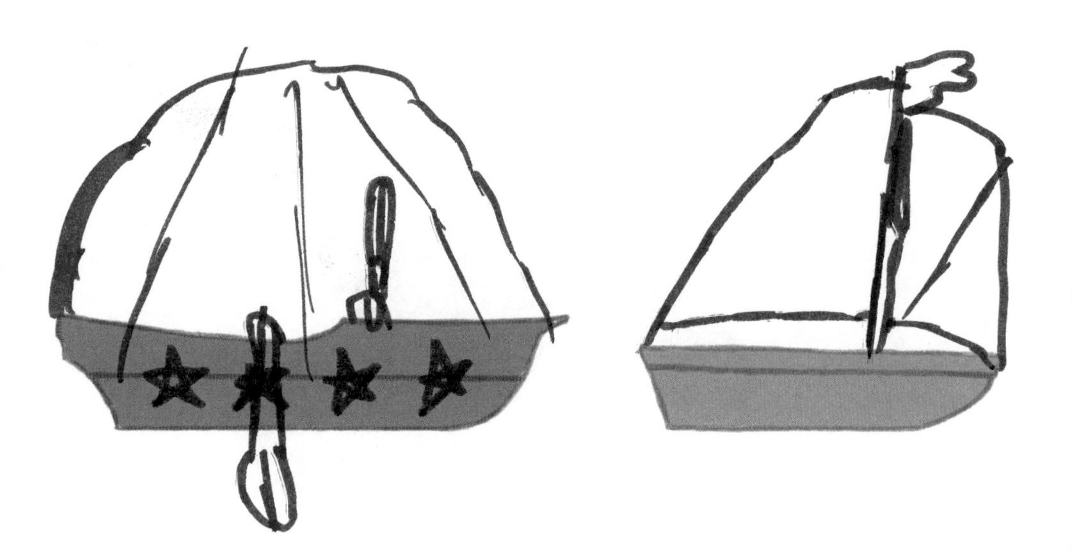

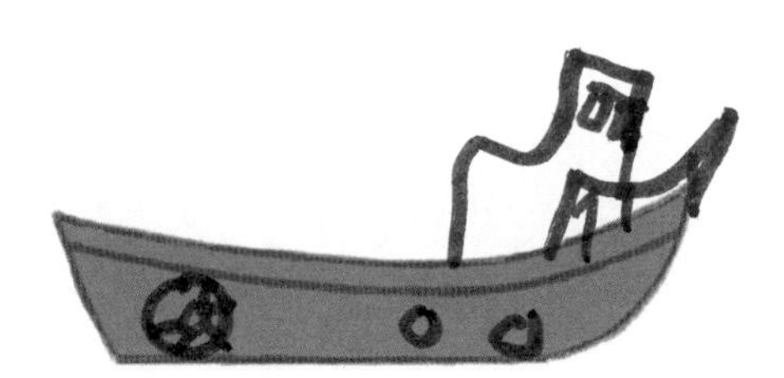

Arrange some presents under the tree.

Customize the T-shirts.

Draw what could be under the ground.

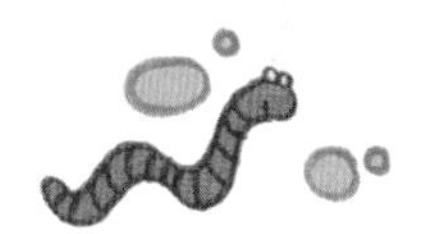

Decorate the winter scarf set.

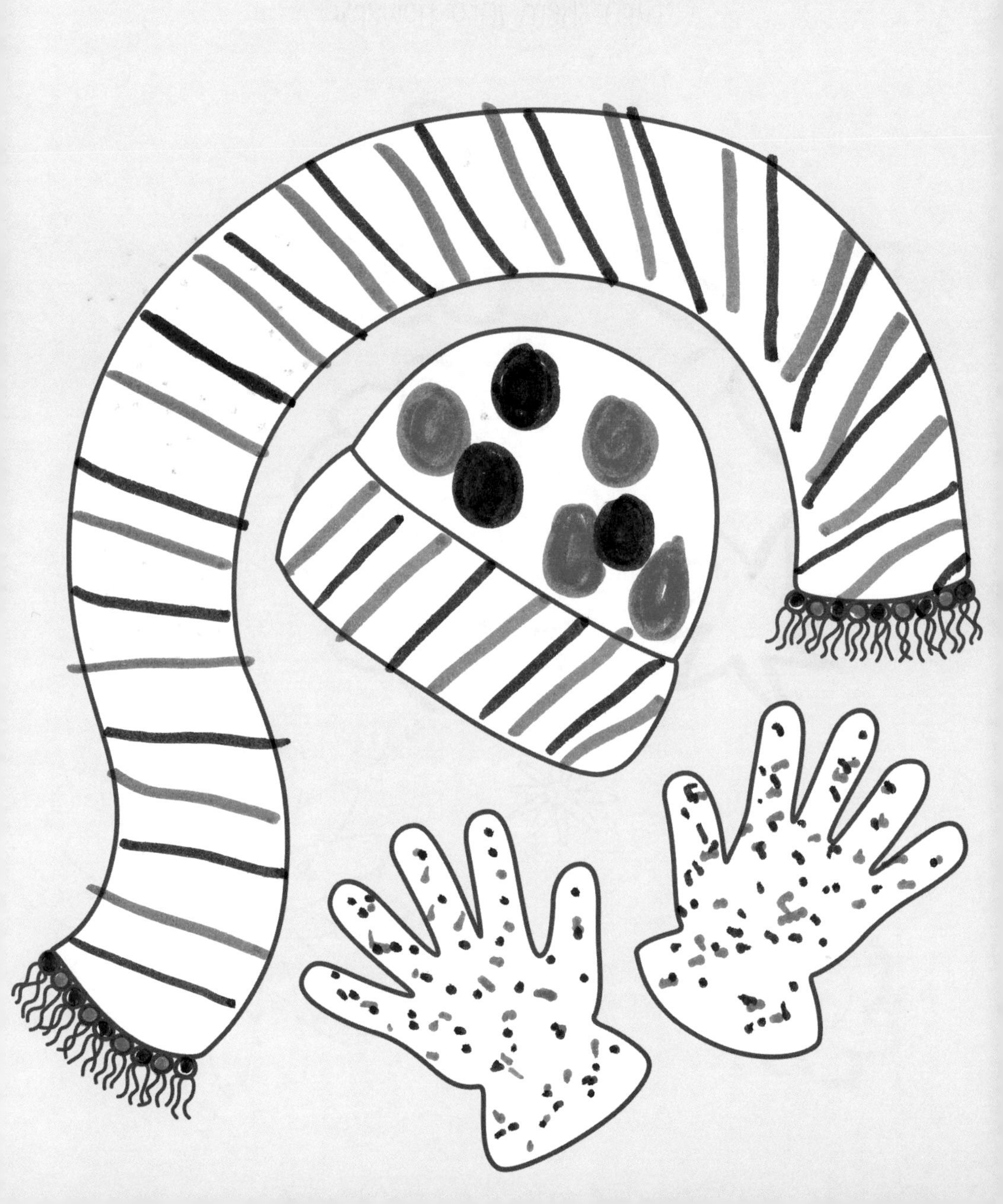

Doodle petals around these circles to turn them into flowers.

Doodle some toppings on the pizza.

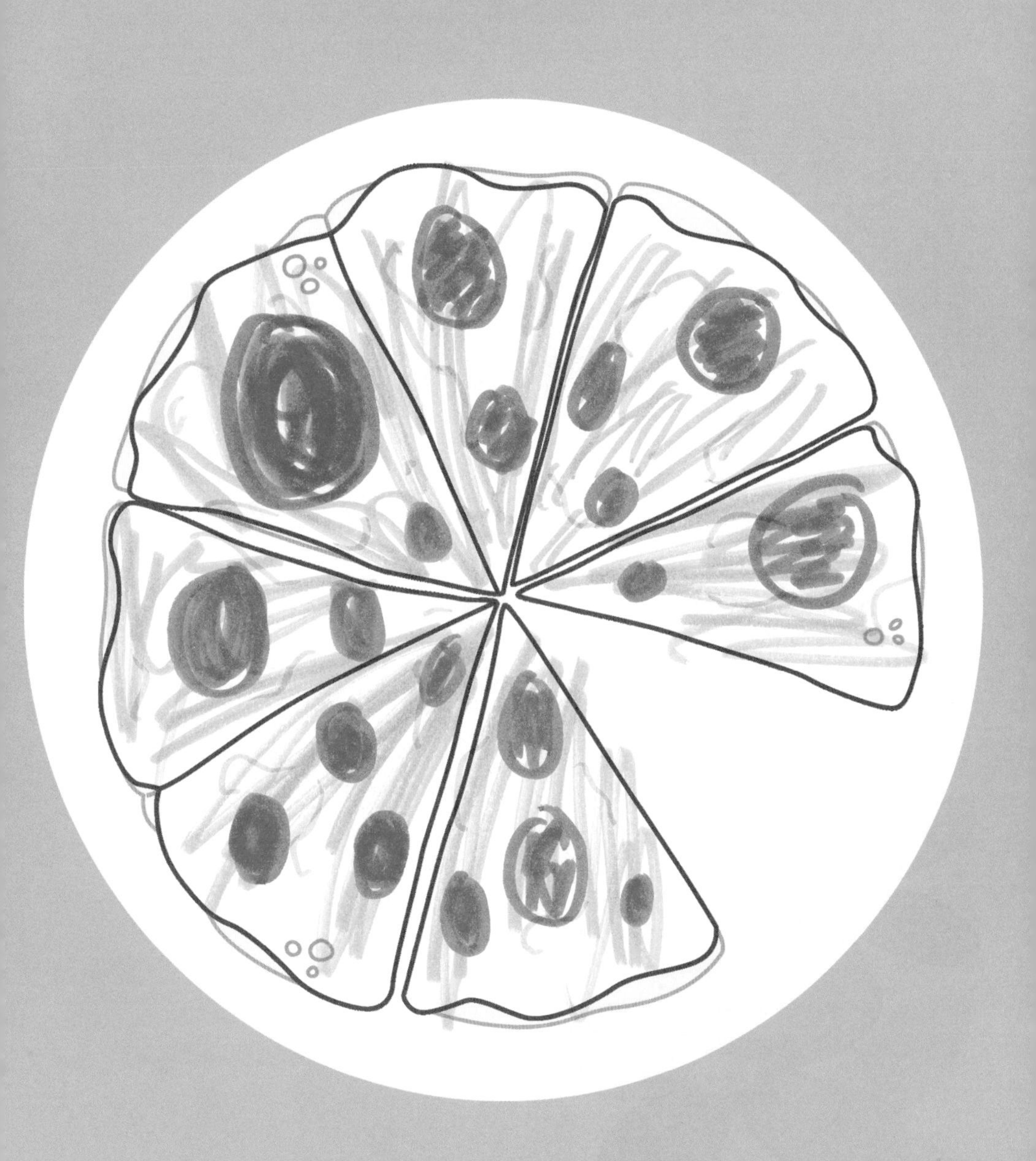

Add some flowers to the display.

Doodle details on the insects.

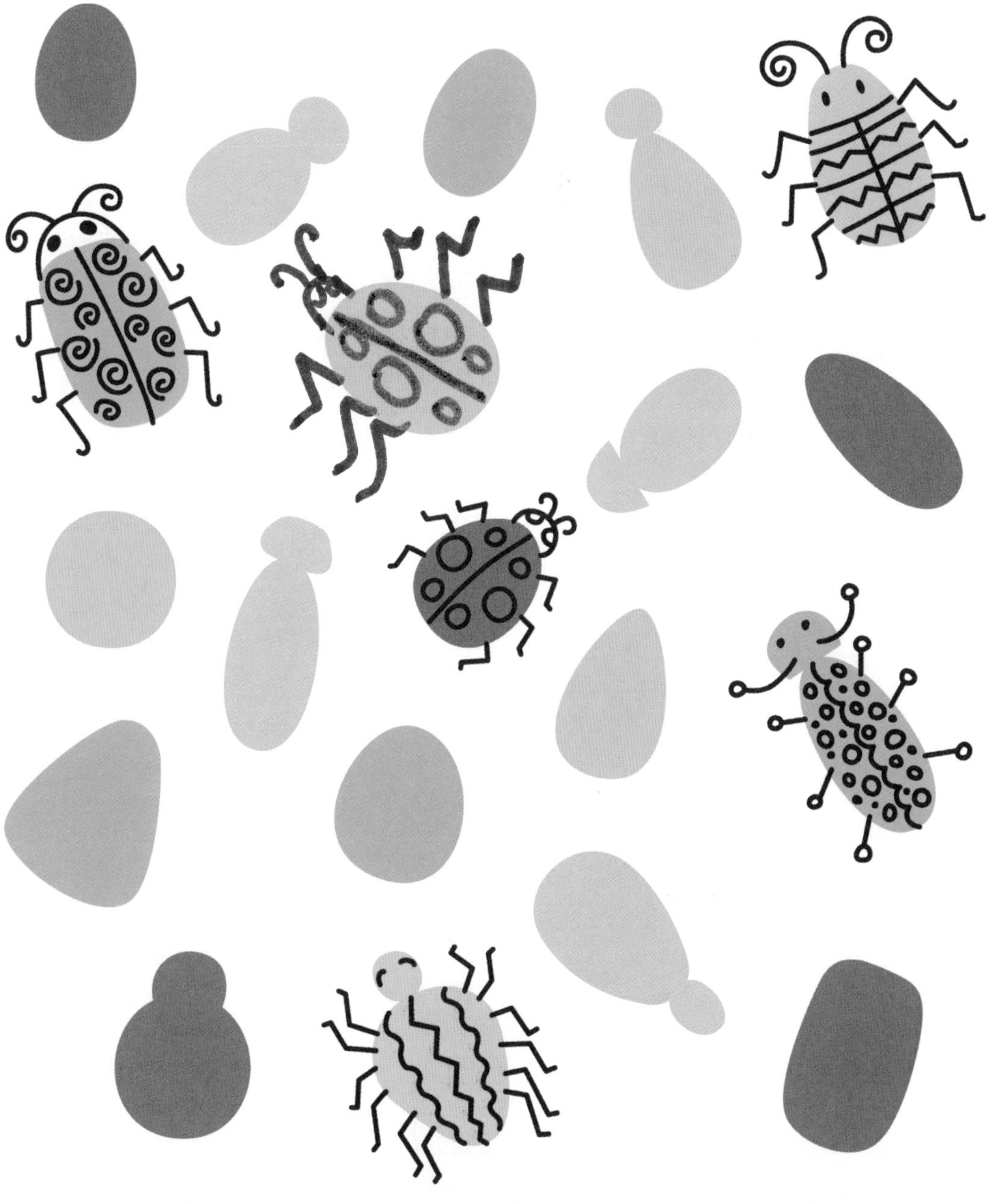

Design a novelty balloon.

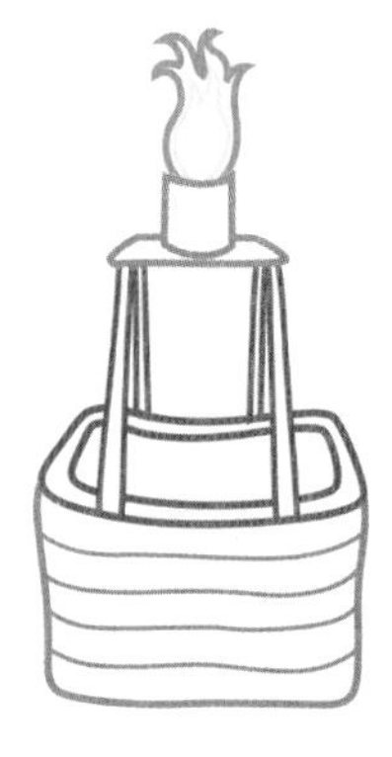

Draw someone who might be in the spotlight.

Fill the page with stars.

Turn these circles into spiders.

Doodle some details on the robot.

Decorate the circles with different doodles.

Doodle giftwrap to match the tags.

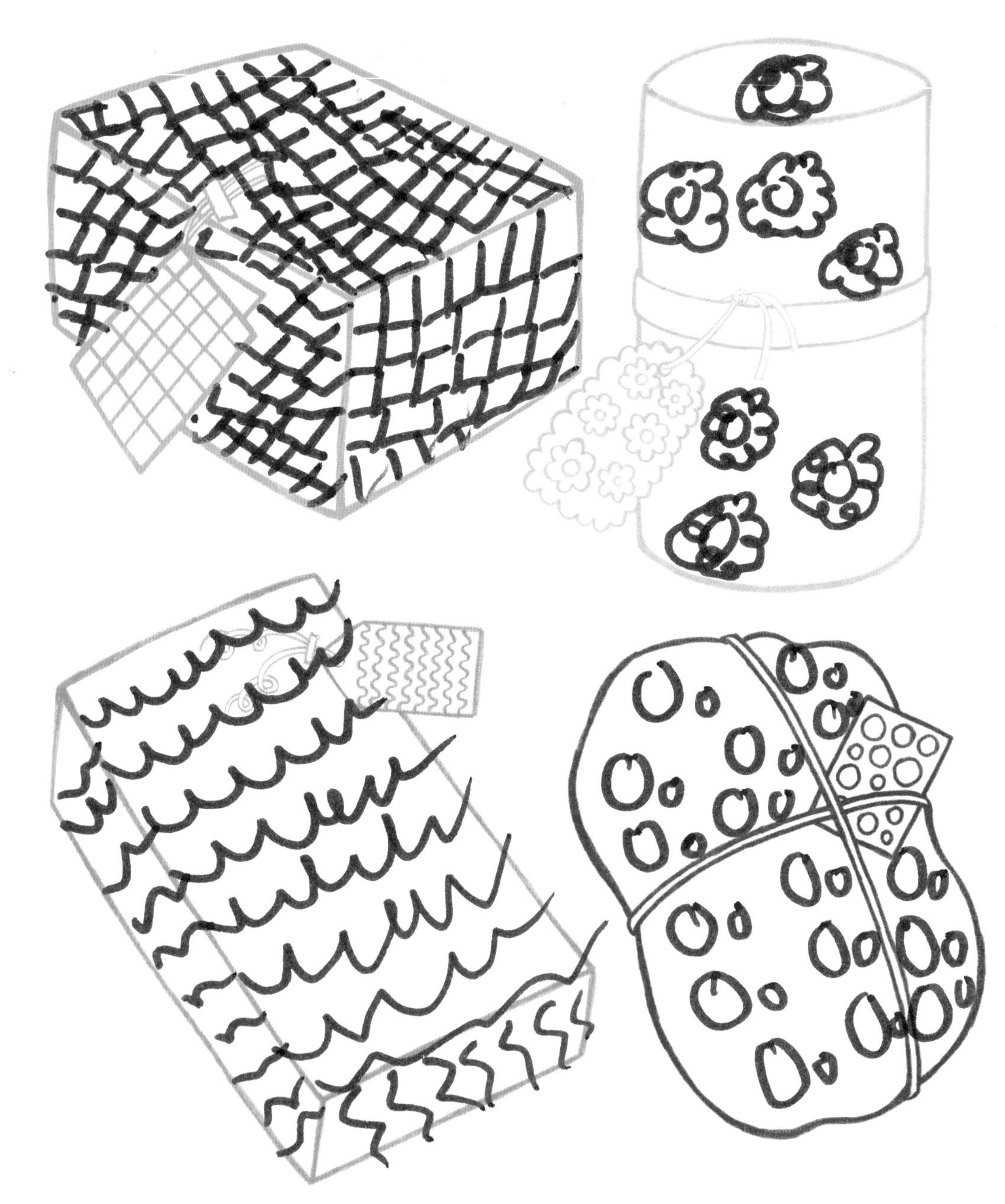

Draw something that might have frightened the swimmer.

Sarah

Give the crooked house more walls and windows, then add a roof.

Doodle spots or other patterns on these fairy toadstools.

Use straight lines to continue the doodle.

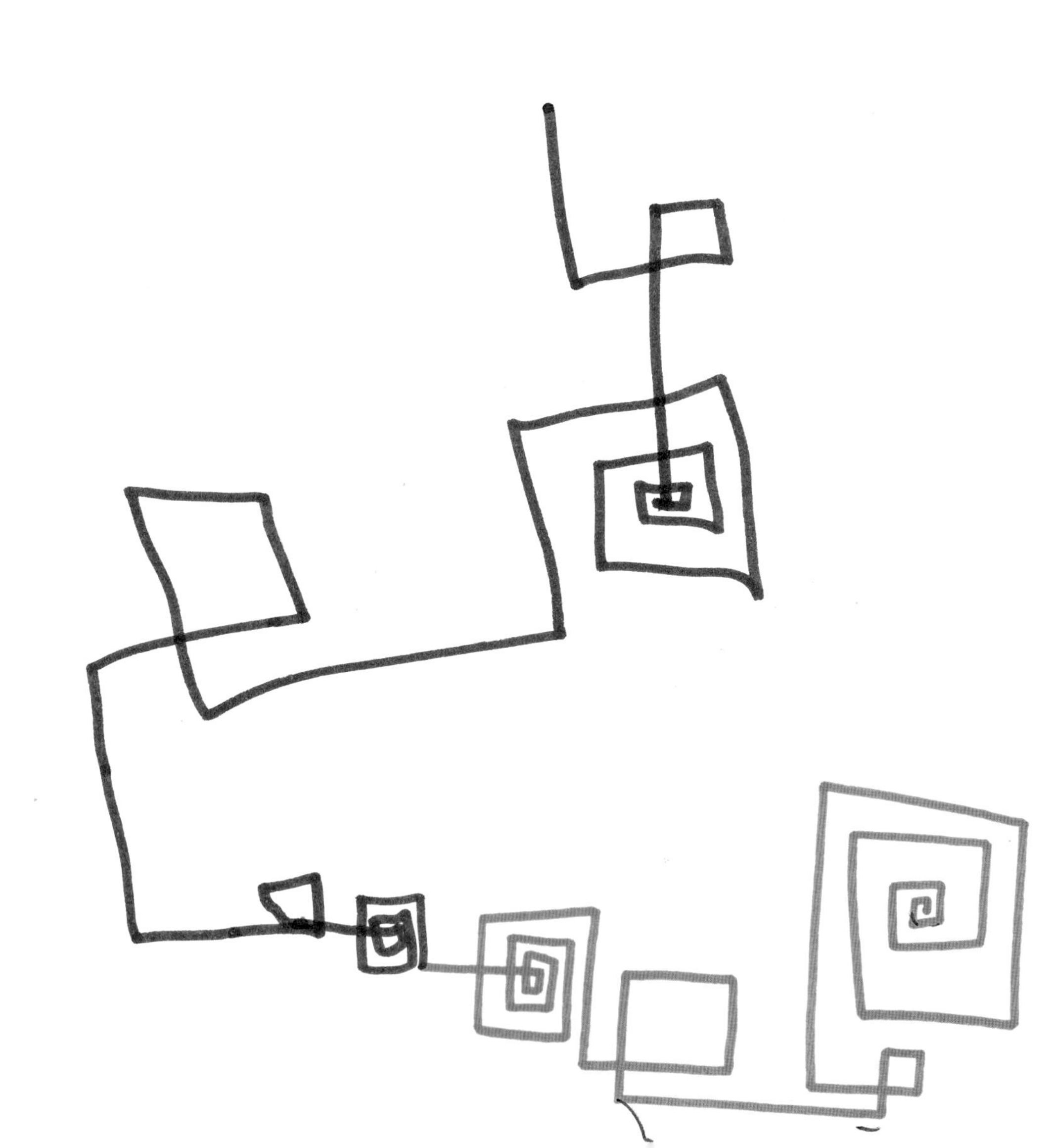

Finish the treasure map.

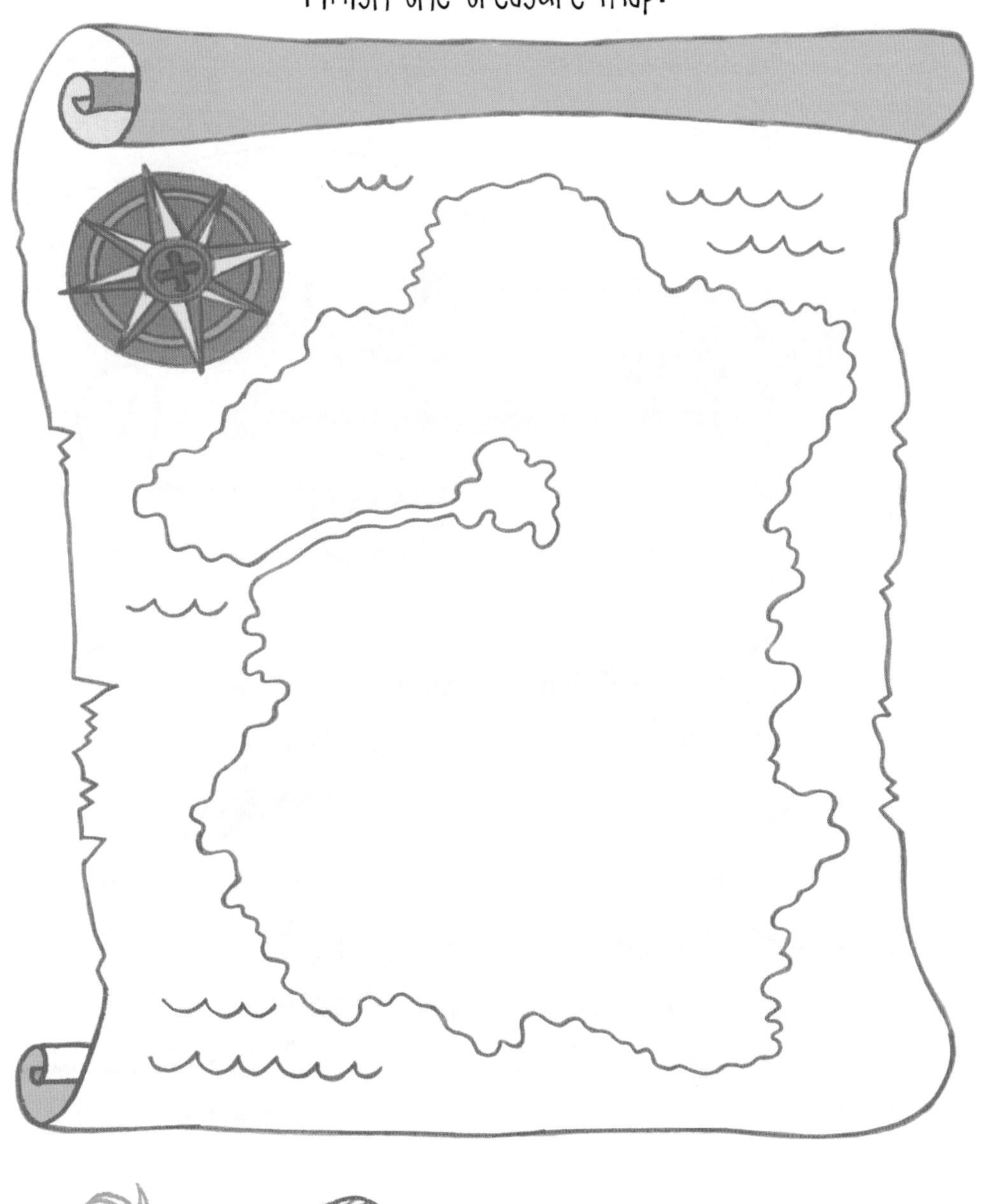

Doodle waves around the surfer.

Doodle some aliens in the spaceships.

Design a lighthouse.

Draw something that might be inside here.

Doodle a prize-winning hedge sculpture.

Decorate the dresses.

Design a lost underwater city.

Fill the sky with fireworks.

Doodle patterns on the carousel horses.

Doodle on the strange plants.

Add more decoration to the gates,
then draw what might lie beyond them.

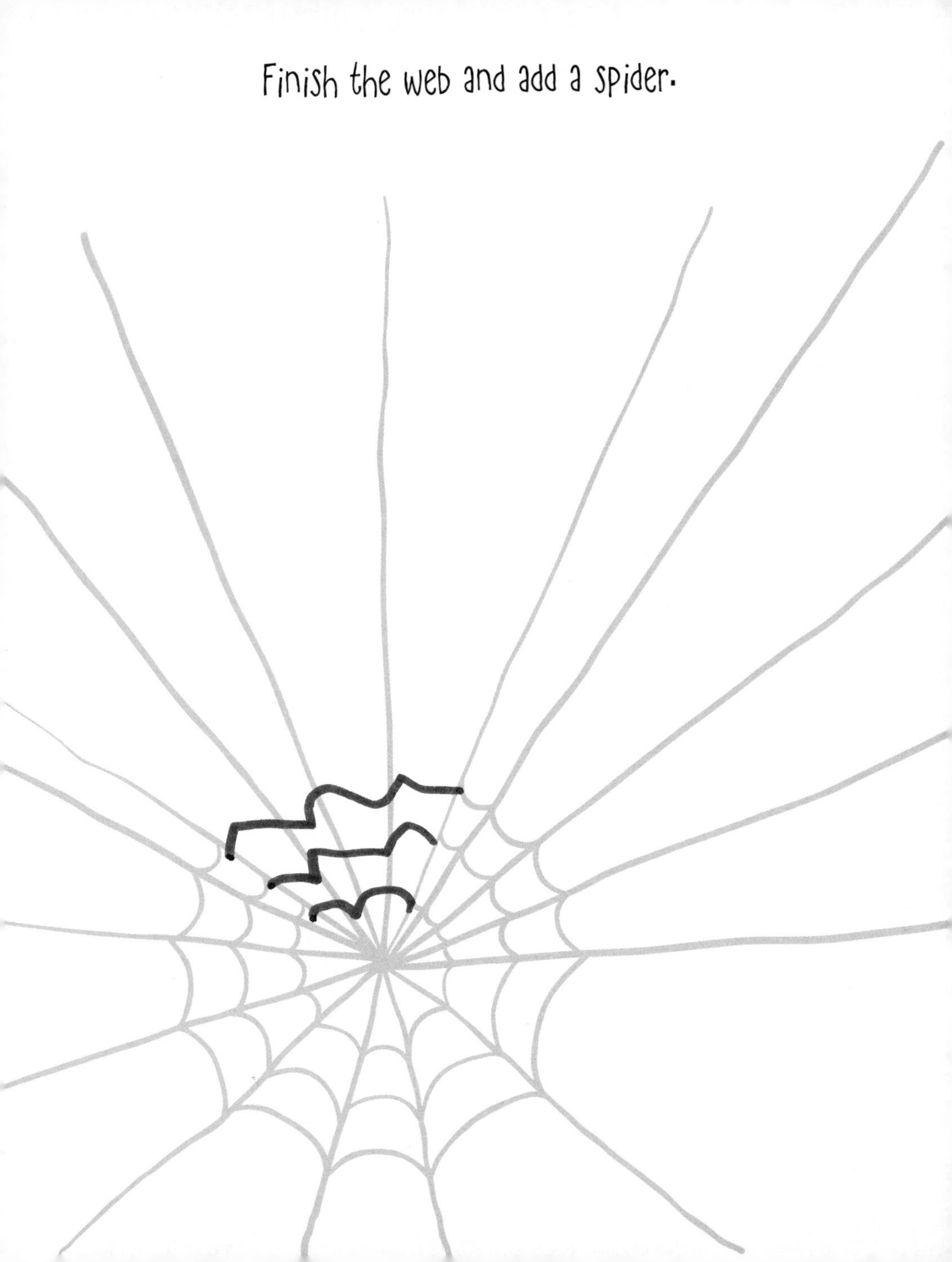
Finish the web and add a spider.

Draw some more astronauts and stars.

Draw some penguins playing and swimming.

Turn this shape into a house or castle.

Fill the page with seashells.

Give these dinosaurs horns, spikes, frills or crests.

Doodle some leaves falling from the tree.

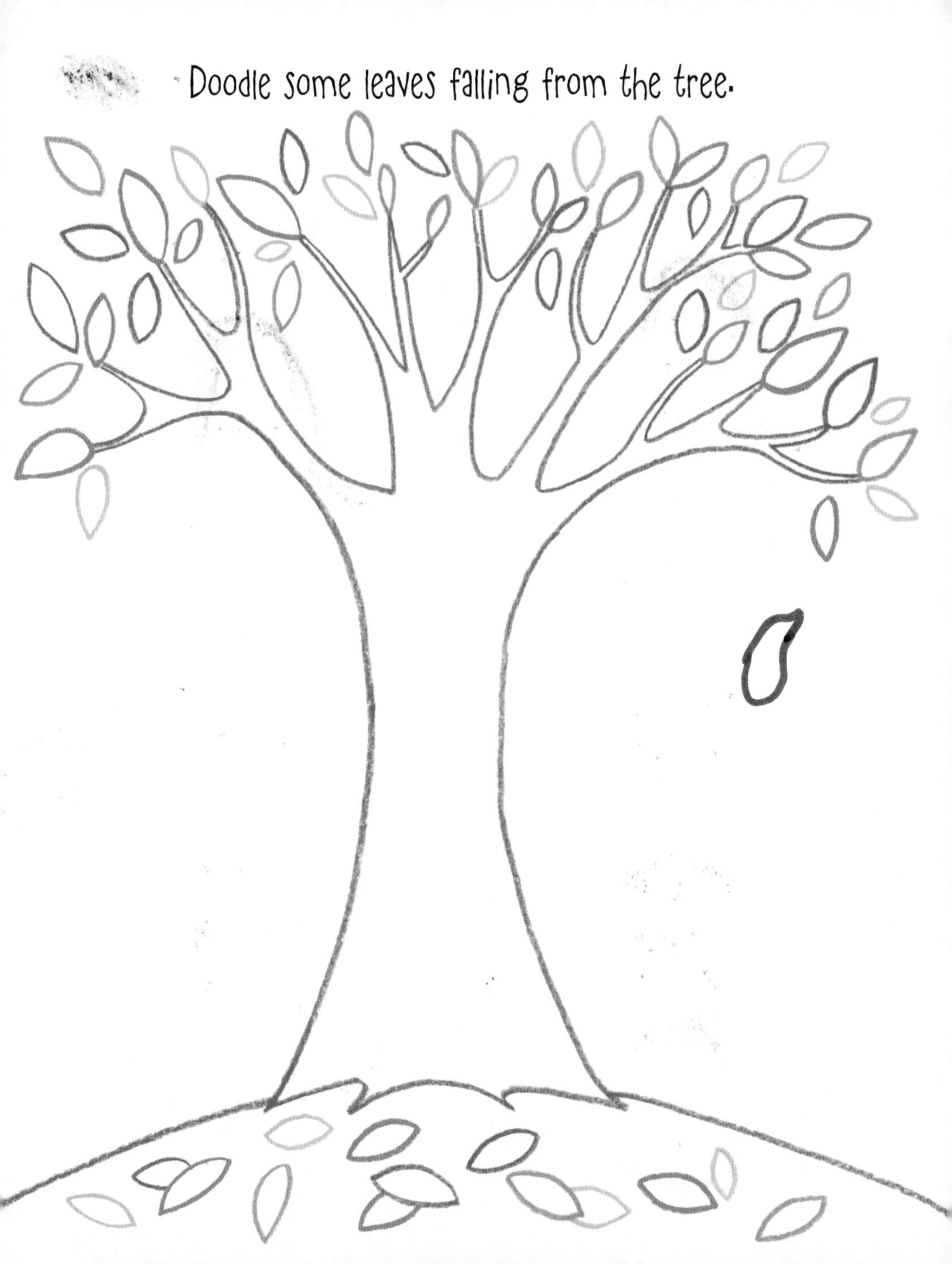

Doodle pictures of yourself and your friends.

Make these shapes into bees.
Hi
Gran
I
knew
you

Decorate the other half of the butterfly.

Turn these shapes into aliens.

Give these monsters faces.

Fill the jars.

Add to this design for an amazing invention. What can it do?

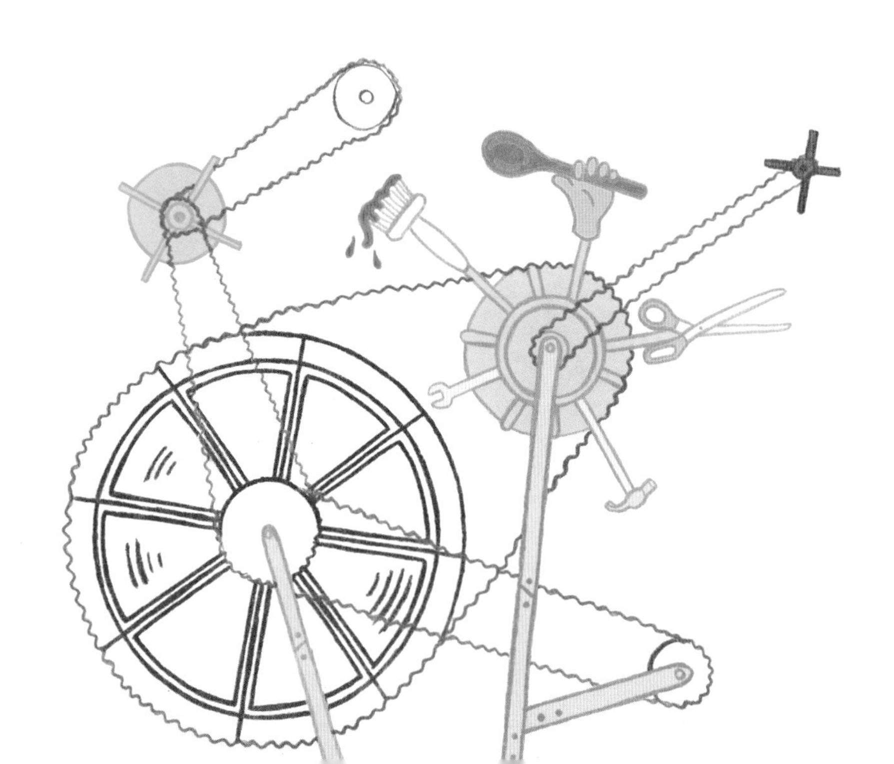

Doodle spikes on the cactus plants.

Decorate the umbrellas.

Fill the flags with patterns.

Turn these shapes into snack bar wrappers.

Doodle what might be happening beneath the city.

Drip, drip, drop... doodle a shower of raindrops.

Decorate the surfboards.

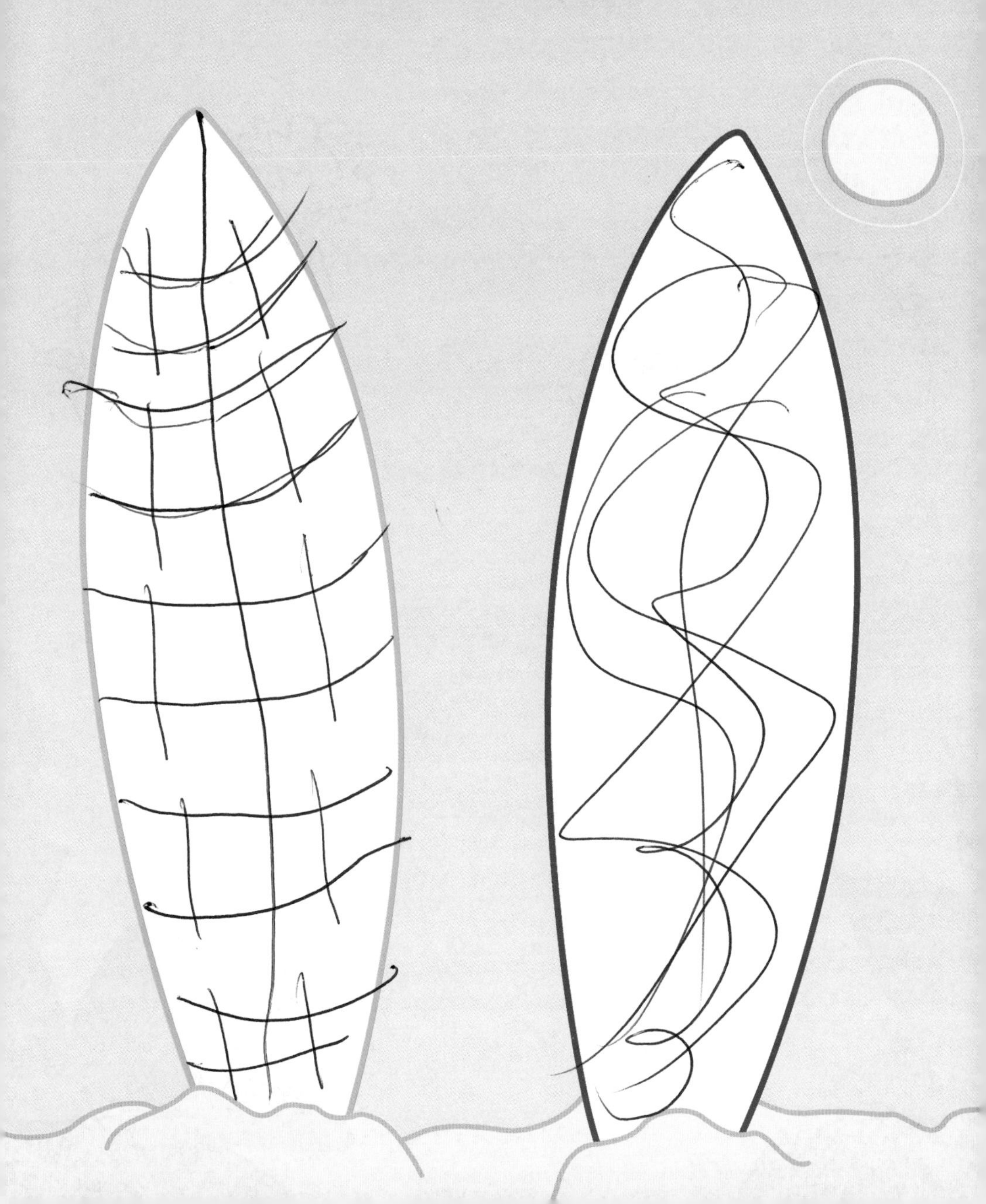

Give the fairies wings and decorate their dresses.

Turn these circles into animals.

Draw what might be hatching out of the egg.

Draw some people from the past.

Add eyes, noses and mouths to the faces.
Grgor
Emma
Kristy

Doodle details on the leaves.

Doodle more stars and planets.

Draw what might be on display in the window.

Create a name plate for your door.

Draw a kite on each string.

Take this line for a walk without crossing
over a line you have already drawn.

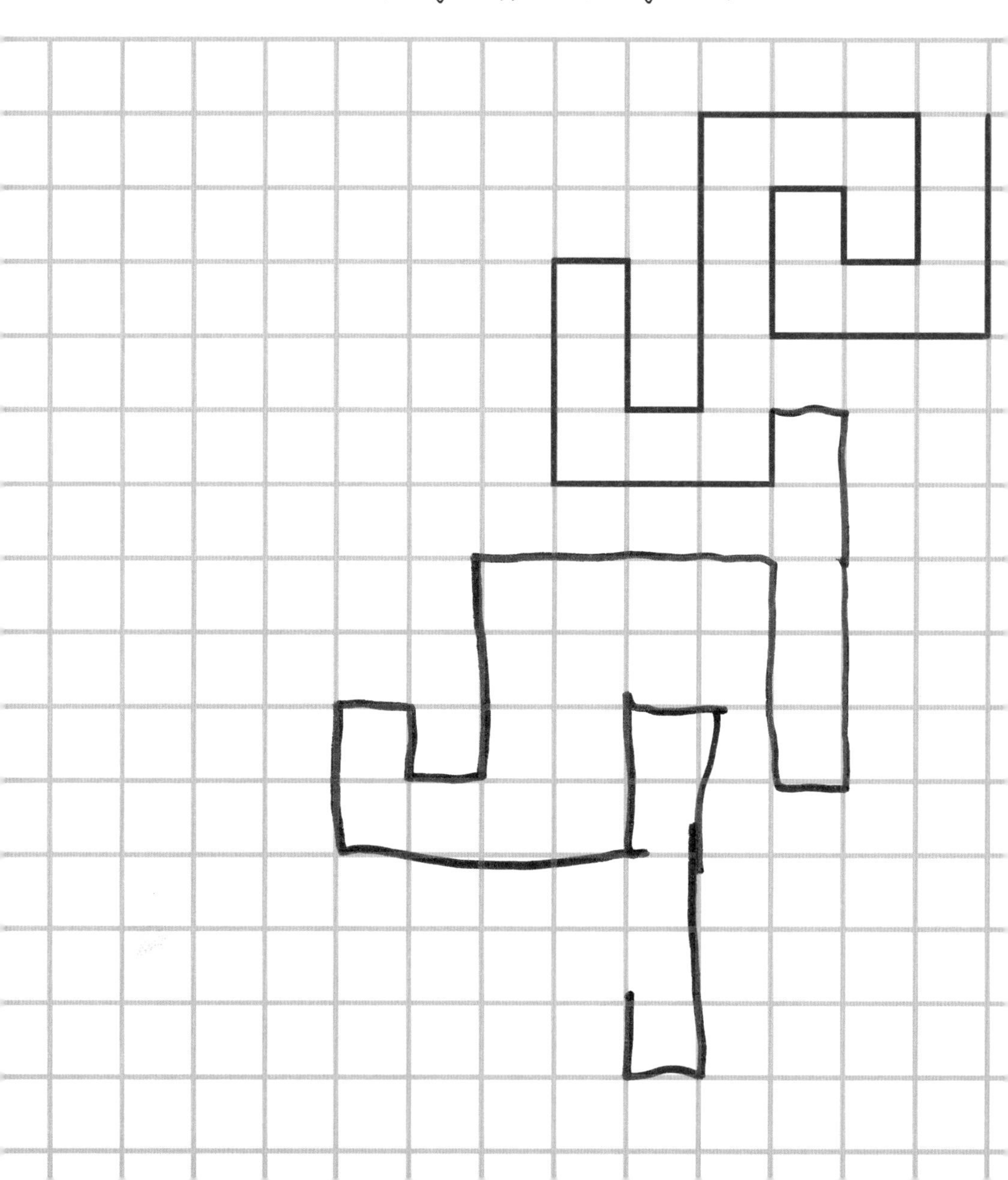

Doodle a cover for your secret diary.

Doodle more feathers on the birds then give each one a juicy worm.

Decorate the crowns with jewels and engravings.

Turn the shapes into birds, or anything else you like.

Decorate the cupcakes.

Draw what might have been discovered in the spotlight.

Transform these shapes into all kinds of insects.

Doodle something for each animal to eat.

Add more patterns to the patchwork quilt.

Give these monsters eyes and teeth.

Turn the circles into cogs.

Design a ballgown.

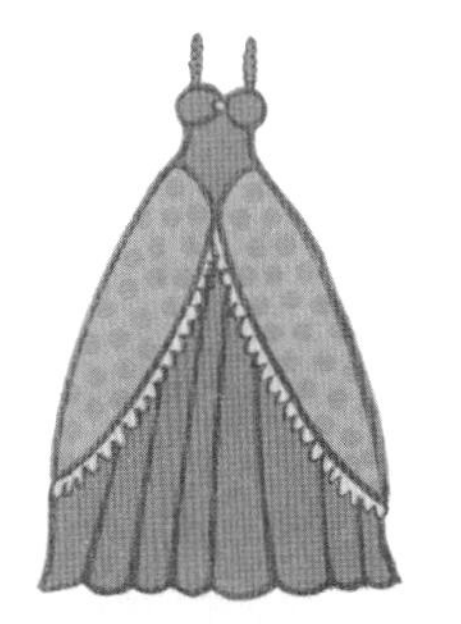

Doodle lots of faces.

Design a space city.

Doodle flowery patterns on the shapes.

Doodle a dancing skeleton.

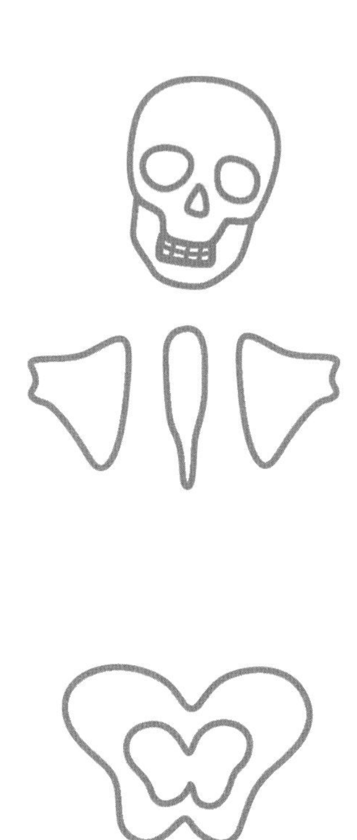

Doodle spectacular tails on the birds.

Draw the other half of the monster.

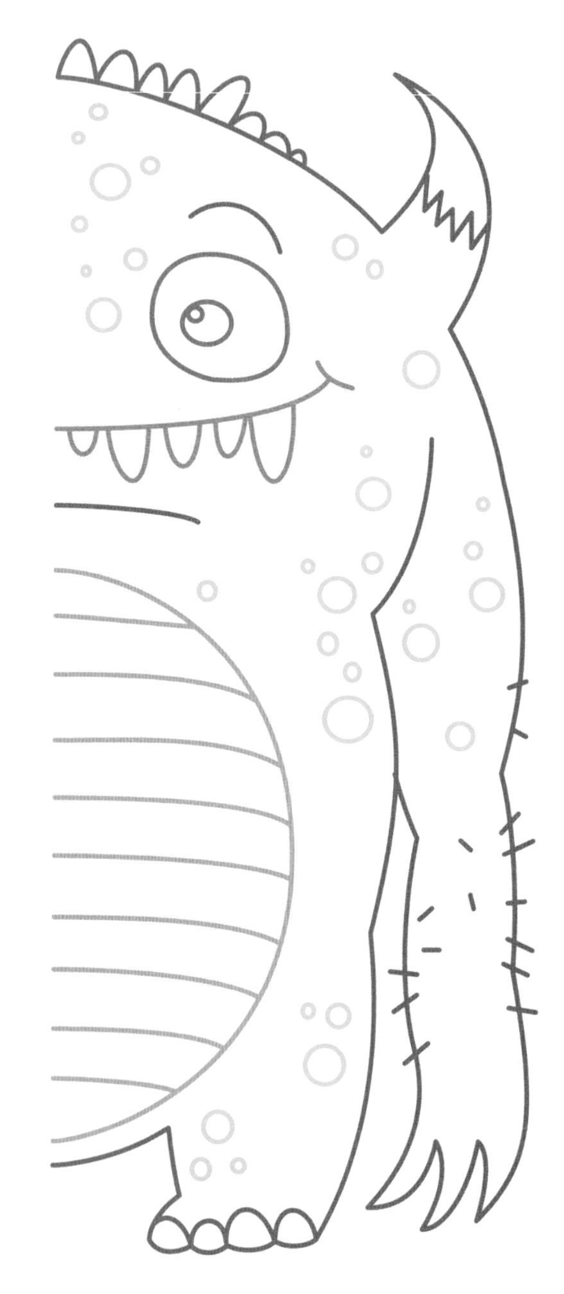

Draw peas in the pods.

Turn this shape into anything you like.

Draw more sharks and waves.

Add charms to the necklace and bracelet.

Design name labels for your friends.

Amy

Ellie

Grace

Cover the tree with leaves and fruits.

Make these shapes look like penguins.

Doodle sea creatures around the eyes.

Doodle on the ship and add some dolphins in the sea.

Doodle this monster's babies.

Turn these shapes into beetles and other bugs.

Add some buildings then doodle lots of windows.

Hi Gran how are you

Doodle pebbles and starfish on the beach.

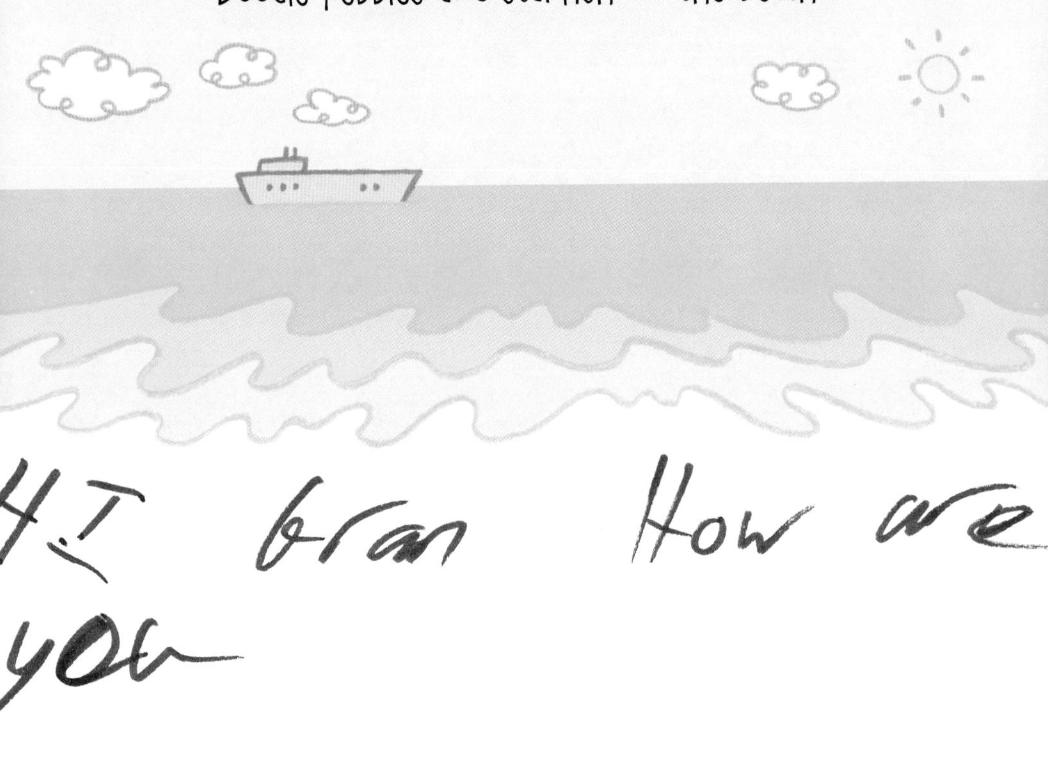

HI Gran How are you

Make the volcano erupt.

Doodle a beautiful bouquet.

Draw some planes.

Cover the leaves with hungry caterpillars.

Add more turrets and towers to the sandcastle.

Add some sheep to the field.

Draw an owner for these teeth.

Design a bridge to cross the river.

Doodle scales on the mermaids.

Doodle some laundry on the line.

Doodle some friends for the dinosaur.

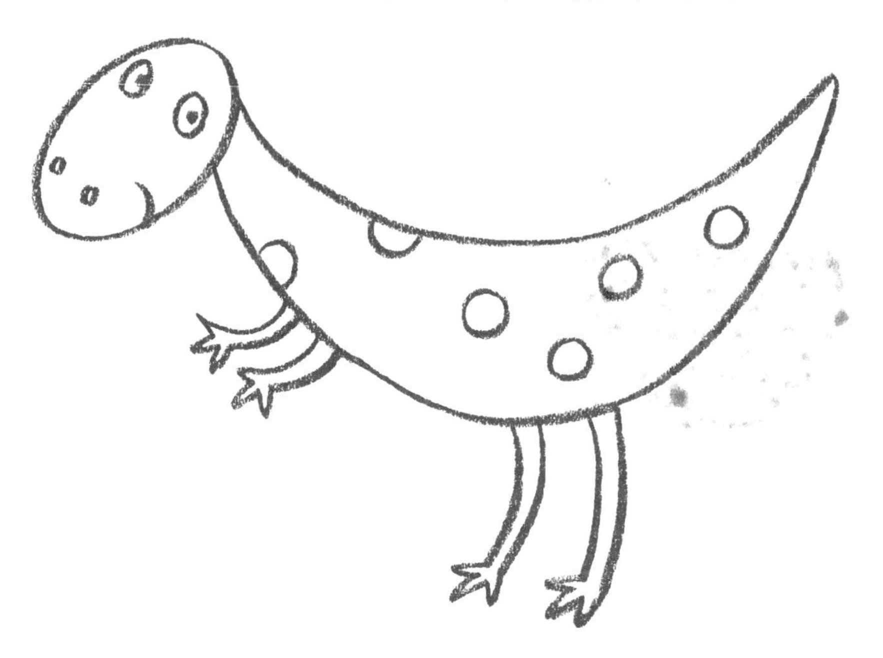

Add faces to the pumpkins.

Fill the page with circles.

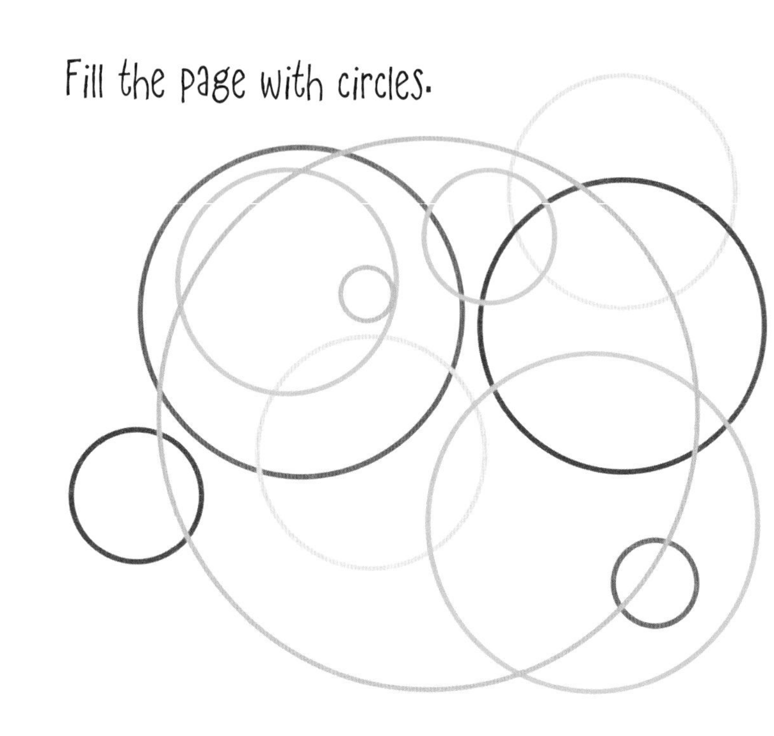

Doodle designs on the stamps.

Add some dolphins.

Doodle patterns on the lizards' tails.

Design a starship.